They all jump on the mat.

Alice swings on the ring.

Kim and Carrots like to watch.

They play on the soft shapes.

Kim climbs over the top . . .

Alice crawls underneath . . .
and Carrots slides down! *Whee!*

Trunk Fun

Text and Art by Stella Levi

Little Elephant has a long trunk.

Long Trunk can swing.
Swish swash swish swash!

Long Trunk can grab food.
Grab munch grab munch!

Long Trunk can sing.
Toot-tooo toot-tooo toot-tooo!

Long Trunk can get Little Elephant
all wet. *SPLASH!*

Over I Go!

by Marilyn Kratz
Art by Alan and Lea Daniel

When I stand and bend down
With my head on the floor,
I tipsy-turn over—
Then do it once more.

Jack Be Nimble

A Mother Goose Rhyme 🐦 Art by David Wenzel

Jack be nimble,
Jack be quick,
Jack jump over
The candlestick.

ch

Kitty's Day

by Valerie S. Biebuyck ♥ Art by Helen Cogancherry

Patting.

Batting.

Lapping.

Napping.

© 2001 by Valerie Biebuyck

Little Mouse

by Edward Lear ❦ Art by Tony Waters

 was once a little mouse.

Mousey,

Bousy,

Sousy,

Mousy,

In the housy,
Little Mouse!

Pillow Tower

by Marybeth Donahue Connelly
Art by Lily Toy Hong

Stack the pillows,
One, two, three.

BABYBUG (ISSN 1077-1131) is published 10 times a year, monthly except for combined May/June and July/August issues, by Carus Publishing Company, Cricket Magazine Group, 315 Fifth Street, Peru, IL 61354. M. Blouke Carus, Chairman; André Carus, President; Jack S. Olbrych, Publisher; Marianne Carus, Editor-in-Chief; Alice Letvin, Editorial Director; Paula Morrow, Editor; Julie Peterson, Assistant Editor; Ron McCutchan, Senior Art Director; Suzanne Beck, Managing Art Director. Volume 7, Number 10; December, 2001. Copyright © 2001, Carus Publishing Company. All rights reserved, including right of reproduction in whole or in part, in any form. All possible care has been taken to trace ownership and secure permission for each selection. **For subscriptions,** address changes, back issues, and customer service: call 1-800-827-0227 or contact us at www.babybugmag.com or write to BABYBUG, P.O. Box 7437, Red Oak, IA